Toledo told to children

TEXT
María Aguado Molina

DRAWINGS
Pilarín Bayés de Luna

EDICIONES MIGUEL SÁNCHEZ

© Ediciones Miguel Sánchez, C.B.

   C/ Marqués de Mondéjar, 44. Granada

© Drawings: Pilarín Bayés de Luna

© Text: María Aguado Molina

   Translation: Babel Traducciones, S.L. (Nicola Jane Graham)

   Photocomposition: Bitono (Paqui Robles)

   Photomechanics: Panalitos S.L.

   Printed by: Gráficas La Madraza. Granada

ISBN: 84-7169-090-X
Depósito Legal: GR 1419/2005

It was a school day. But not just any day. They had gone on a trip! Ali, Sara and Marcos' teacher was taking them to Toledo, along with the other pupils in class 6.

The journey from Madrid to Toledo is not very long and the scenery along the way is beautiful.

"Look out of the windows, children!" the teacher said in the bus. "Toledo is on a hill and you can see the Tagus valley from the top. Do you know the names of the other places the river passes through, where it ends, how many...?"

The teacher always took advantage of any situation to ask classroom stuff. Meanwhile, the children saw that they were getting closer and closer to a small but very compact city, as if it were squashed into a cup, with ramparts and several towers jutting out. Later they found out that these towers belonged to the *Alcazar* (a fortified palace) and the Cathedral.

The bus stopped in front of a beautiful gate, with two keeps and a coat of arms with an eagle.

"That is the *Puerta de Bisagra*, which means hinge in English, and it dates from the reign of Charles V. The two-headed eagle is not a monster from a fairytale. It is the imperial coat of arms."

What a lot of things the teacher knew! But the most exciting thing was that they were going to visit a city all together, walk through its streets, meet its people...

Ali, Marcos and Sara had been very good friends since the beginning of the school year and they went everywhere together. That was why they were the ones to see the old man.

They had walked quite a long way along a steep street, the Calle Real del Arrabal, so that they could climb up from the valley to the historic city and they had stopped to rest next to one of the gates in the ramparts. It was one of the most impressive gates the children had ever seen.

"That is the *Puerta del Sol*, which means Gate of the Sun," their teacher told them. "It was rebuilt in the 14th century in the typical Mudéjar style of Toledo. We know this because the historians and archaeologists have found out that it was standing in the 10th century, in Islamic times, and that since then it has been used to access the city and as a defence system. Can you see the merlons? The gate's name comes from the paintings on the tympanum (the triangle with reliefs inside that circular medallion) and which were added later. What do the painted figures represent?"

"The Sun and the Moon," everyone chorused to answer their teacher's question. You could actually make them out quite easily.

And there, underneath the gate, was the man. He was old, with white hair and he had a stick. He was smiling all the time and seemed very friendly. He had a street stall with souvenirs of Toledo, which he was selling to tourists.

The children went up to him out of curiosity and Ali, who was the most forward, asked him:

"Are you from here?"

"Yes, of course. I'm from Toledo. Always have been!" the stallkeeper replied very proudly. And Sara, who didn't have any problems chatting to people either, wanted to know: "Is it true that

this is a beautiful city with a great deal of history?"

"It is much more than beautiful. It's magical! You see, first the Celtiberians lived here, the settlers in the Iberian Peninsula before the Romans came and conquered them. Then, the Romans built a city with ramparts, houses, a theatre and a circus, temples and aqueducts for the water... And all this happened 2200 years ago! A few centuries later (between the 6th and the 8th) the Visigoths turned it into the capital of their kingdom and then it was conquered by the Arabs. So you see, there had to be a reason for Toledo being surrounded by these tremendous ramparts.

The emirs from Cordoba took control of the city in the 8th century, but don't think that the population didn't make a stand, because they did! The rebellions against the emirs first and against the caliphs from Cordoba afterwards continued for another two hundred years. Ab al Rahman III himself had to come here to consolidate Muslim control. Do you know who that important figure in the history of Al Andalus was?"

"Of course we do! We studied about him in class," the children replied.

"Perfect! You are very intelligent children! So, not long afterwards, at the beginning of the 11th century, when the Caliphate of Cordoba broke up into many different kingdoms (called *taifas*), Toledo became the capital of one of them. Since then, it has been a rich and flourishing city because of its culture, craftwork..., a place where Muslims, Christians (called Mozarabs) and Jews all lived together. Controlled by the Muslims, of course. What do you think about that?"

"That must have been a bit difficult, mustn't it? There are always stories on the TV about confrontations in Palestine and all that," said Ali, as this was a subject close to home.

"Well, there were problems then too. The Christians and the Jews paid more taxes and they lived in special quarters in the city. They didn't mix together, but they could share the city and at the same time keep their customs and beliefs."

"The old stallkeeper also knows a lot," Marcos thought to himself. He was a little too shy to join in the conversation.

"And then what happened?" Sara asked impatiently.

"At the beginning of the 12th century, the Christian king, Alphonse VI of Castile conquered the city from the Arabs. I suppose you also know that the Christian and the Andalusian kingdoms fought each other constantly in the Middle Ages in order to possess the land of the entire Peninsula. But they all continued to live together in Toledo. The Muslim (they were called Mudéjar then) and the Jewish communities were then the ones that had to pay special taxes and the Christians took over the positions of power, although there were also Christian peasants and craftworkers, just as there were Muslim and Jewish ones. Don't think that they were so different! In any case, the Jews specialised more in craftwork and business, money lending... and some of the families became very rich."

All this knowledge was starting to make the children's heads spin, but it was so unusual for someone they didn't know and who was so educated to pay them any attention! Who was that man? Had he been a teacher once too? What was he doing now, selling souvenirs in the street? It was such an exciting mystery!

The old man was very pleased to have such an interested and attentive audience, so he continued to give them details about life at that time.

"You could still see Islamic culture everywhere. The majority of the medieval buildings in Toledo are Mudéjar in style. I'm sure your teacher will explain all about that. But from the 13th century it began to be mixed with styles from Central Europe, Italy, the Eastern Mediterranean and from the faraway and exotic Constantinople.

In Toledo, King Alphonse X, who ended up being known by everyone as 'The Wise', created the 'School of Translators'. Do you know what they did there and in the Court? Well, they gathered all the main intellectuals of the time there, regardless of whether they were Arabs, Jews or Christians, from here or from abroad, so that they could discuss astronomy, law, medicine, literature, philosophy... They also translated the main works by the most important authors in ancient Greece and Rome (their names were Aristotle, Ptolemy and Hippocrates) into Spanish and Latin. It was a very important time in Toledo's history."

The old man continued with his history lesson.

"The coexistence between the Jews and the Mudéjars deteriorated in the 14th century until the Catholic Monarchs, Isabella of Castile and Ferdinand of Aragon, expelled them from Spain in the 15th century. Toledo became more important during their reign, because it was the headquarters of the Courts of Castile for some years and later, when their grandson Emperor Charles V was on the throne, Toledo was given the title of Imperial City, just when the Spanish Empire was expanding, with the conquest of America. So the city's inhabitants managed to get the crown and the Church interested in constructing official buildings, palaces and churches, new gates in the ramparts..."

"Like the *Puerta de Bisagra*, which our teacher told us about!" Ali said.

"That's right. Toledo became one of the most important cities in Spain, with over fifty thousand inhabitants. Later, from the 17th century, it started to decline because it was affected by the crisis of the whole empire and because Philip II had transferred the capital to Madrid in the 16th century.

People started to leave the city then and it became smaller and agriculture-based. Religious orders flooded the streets, building convents and monasteries everywhere (you're bound to see them) and it didn't recover until almost the present day. Even then, the city's most important figures made some contributions in the 18th century: factories to promote industry, hospitals to improve people's quality of life, a university... but they didn't manage to make the city progress. And in the 19th century, as a result of the War of Independence against the French, the majority

of the buildings collapsed and many sites became public areas. Later, Toledo became the capital of the province. It again started to play an important role in culture and politics and the economy grew. Many barracks and military academies were located in the city.

In the Civil War... you know when that was, don't you? 1936 to 1939. The city suffered a long siege. The soldiers took refuge in the *Alcazar*, Emperor Charles V's fortified palace, which was quite destroyed. It was rebuilt after the war.

"Well, it means that the whole city, its buildings, its streets.. everything belongs to every human being and it forms part of everyone's historical and cultural memory and it has to be respected and preserved for our children, grandchildren..."

"That's wonderful!" the children shouted.

But in the end, from the sixties in the 20th century, economic development and emigration from the countryside to the city started to bring people, who settled outside the ramparts. After the dictatorship had ended and with the arrival of democracy, this city of monuments became the capital of the Autonomous Community of Castile La Mancha and it was given the title of World Heritage Site in 1986. What do you think of that?"

The others were still eating their breakfast sandwiches sitting nearby, so they had a little more time to ask the very nice old man some more things:

"And how can you remember all that?"

"Fantastic! We're going to visit a very old place where lots of things have happened!" Sara said excitedly. Marcos plucked up the courage to say something and asked: "What does World Heritage Site mean?"

"Oh well, children. My memory is not what it was. Despite everything, I can remember my knowledge of history. But I'm forgetting the details, the small things that have marked my life in this city. I wanted to write my past down, but I can't remember some things about special places where I have experienced equally special moments."

"What places were they? What do you need? We could help you!"

"Would you like to? Would you like to be my eyes and help me to revive my memory of some images in three important places that I can't visit now? I can't leave my stall."

"Of course we would. We're going to go round the city. Tell us what we have to find."

The three children were getting more and more excited. Now they could help that man who had told them so many things and who they had warmed to. They could be useful to him.

"You see, I can only manage to remember bits and pieces. First, I need to know where some palm tree leaves are represented underneath a rope. I can only remember the image, somewhere in the darkness of the oldest building in Toledo that has been preserved from the Islamic age. They used to kneel under them to pray and I was happy there too.

The second thing I need to remember is which figure is represented on the ceiling before the Chapel of St. Ildephonsus, opposite the altar called *El Transparente*, in the Cathedral, because I learnt something very important there.

And third, how many windows there are over the arches that open onto the niche where

the Jews kept the Torah in the Synagogue that Samuel Levi, the King's treasurer, built. If I can find all this out, I will be able to realise something important."

"We'll draw what we see when we find these images. I've got my exercise book with me," Marcos added.

RESTOS ALCANTARILLA ROMANA

The break was over. The teacher called all the children together to start climbing up to a gate called the *Puerta de Valmardón*. Meanwhile, she was also explaining the history of Toledo, but Ali, Sara and Marcos, who now already knew it all, because they had just listened to it and learnt it, were thinking about something else. They had to remember that they had agreed to meet the stallkeeper in the street called Calle de los Alamillos after lunch to give him the information he wanted.

They went through the gate in the ramparts, where archaeologists had pieced together the puzzle of the past very scientifically when they discovered a Roman sewer outlet. Then the children saw a lovely narrow street, steep and silent. On the left there was an even lovelier brick building, enclosed behind some railings.

"This is the Calle del Cristo de la Luz, one of the oldest in Toledo, with the original route from the Islamic age. It is

ABSIDE
AÑADIDO
AL PRIMITIVO
EDIFICIO ISLAMICO

CRISTOS

virtually the same as it was 1,000 years ago," the teacher explained.

The children's imagination started to fly thinking about the thousands of people that must have walked this way since then.

"And this brick building is the **Mosque of Cristo de la Luz**, which means Christ of the Light. It is the oldest Islamic building still standing intact in Toledo, dating from the 10th century, although it was altered in the 12th century by the Christians to convert it into a church and they added an apse

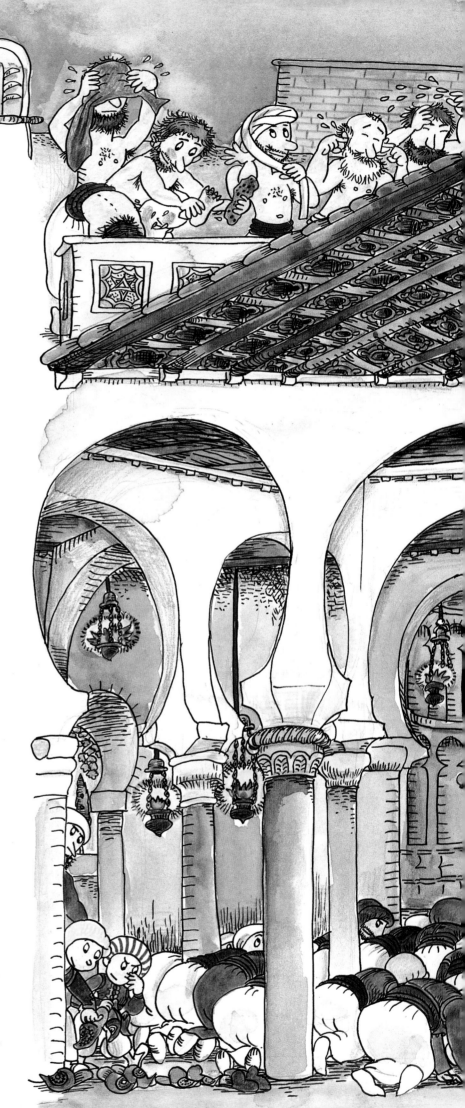

decorated in Mudéjar style and some Romanesque paintings inside."

"Hey," said Marcos. "This must be the first place the old man mentioned for his memories."

"Let's get nearer to the facade. You can see the inside from the outside. It was originally square in plan and the ceiling was divided into nine ribbed domes, each one different from the others. There are four columns supporting the ceiling. They have Visigoth capitals with motifs taken from nature, although they are very geometrical. Can you see the leaves of the plants carved into the stone? The arches are horseshoe or multifoil, which means that the arch has lots of lobes next to each other. They look just like earlobes, don't they?"

The pupils thought this was funny. They all started to study the ears of the child next to them.

"Sometimes the bricks forming the arches are two different colours, alternately red and white, in the style of the Mosque in Cordoba, which also dates from the caliphs' time. In the main facade, you could enter the mosque through three arches, each one with a different shape. Look carefully! One is a horseshoe, one is semicircular and the last one is the multifoil arch with all the lobes (the children still giggled when they heard this). At the top you can see the typical Mudéjar

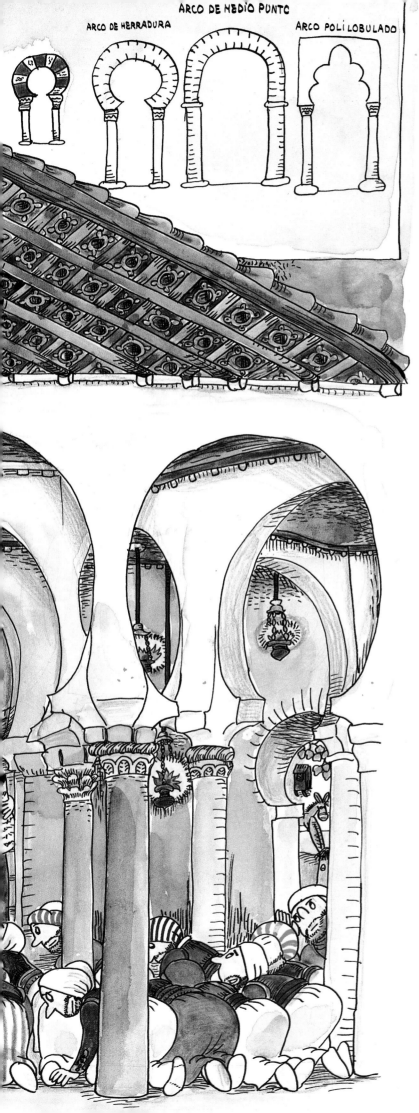

decoration and an inscription in Arabic stating the names of the builder, the architect and the construction date."

"Look at that capital!" Sara said, pointing to one of the four they could see. "There are leaves and they are underneath something that looks like a coiled rope."

"Yes! They could be palm leaves," Ali said. Marcos started to draw it immediately.

They had found the first of the things the old man had forgotten. And it hadn't been that difficult. Fantastic, the three of them thought, while the teacher explained a little more about the building:

"This mosque is very small, isn't it? It must have been the oratory or the small private chapel of an important noble family in Toledo whose members would come here to pray every day. They would wash following a rite to purify and clean themselves with water they got from a well behind the building and they used to kneel facing the east, which is where Mecca is, and say their prayers. Mecca is the Muslims' holy city. In the Middle Ages religion was an intense experience and these rites formed part of this people's daily life."

"How interesting!" Sara thought. And suddenly a question crossed her mind:

"Why was it called Christ of the Light if it was an Arab mosque?"

Her teacher explained that it had a Christian name because it had been converted into a church and had been dedicated to an image of Christ on the Cross and to Our Lady of Light.

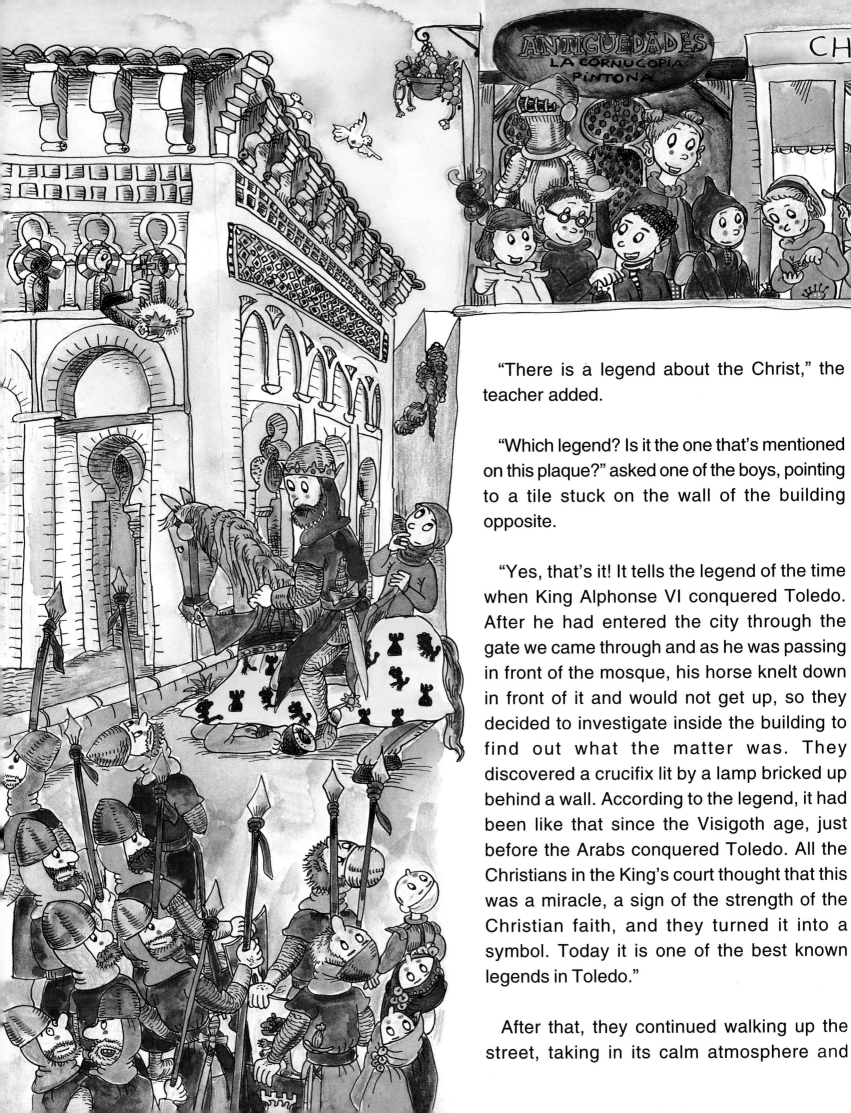

"There is a legend about the Christ," the teacher added.

"Which legend? Is it the one that's mentioned on this plaque?" asked one of the boys, pointing to a tile stuck on the wall of the building opposite.

"Yes, that's it! It tells the legend of the time when King Alphonse VI conquered Toledo. After he had entered the city through the gate we came through and as he was passing in front of the mosque, his horse knelt down in front of it and would not get up, so they decided to investigate inside the building to find out what the matter was. They discovered a crucifix lit by a lamp bricked up behind a wall. According to the legend, it had been like that since the Visigoth age, just before the Arabs conquered Toledo. All the Christians in the King's court thought that this was a miracle, a sign of the strength of the Christian faith, and they turned it into a symbol. Today it is one of the best known legends in Toledo."

After that, they continued walking up the street, taking in its calm atmosphere and

beauty, until they came to another, called Calle de los Alfileritos, which means little pins.

"This is another very old street. It was the parapet walk of the ramparts, where the soldiers on guard duty used to walk."

The teacher then asked her pupils:

"Do you know why some streets in historic cities are named after objects or professions? Well, because in the Middle Ages (and afterwards as well), the streets were known by the activity of the craftworkers that had their homes or their workshops there. Seamstresses lived in this street and a little further on is the Calle de la Sillería (street of chairs) and the Calle del Comercio (business). Other streets lead to this one called: Tornería (of lathes), Chapinería (of chapines, which are a type of clog), Cordonería (of shoelaces)... Can you imagine the craftsmen in their workshops, with their doors and windows looking out onto the street, making shoelaces and shoes? This was also the area where the mesones (restaurants) and the bazaars (shops) were and it still is today, isn't it?"

The route they followed took them through one of the most famous squares in the city, the *Plaza de Zocodover*. As *zoco* means market, it is not surprising that this was the place where the shopkeepers gathered on Tuesdays from the 15th century. In fact, it had been used as a marketplace since Islamic times and its name comes from the Arabic "*Suk al Dawl*", which means the beast or cattle market.

PALAC
DE LA
AUDIENC

And after walking for a long time they came to the **Cathedral**. They walked underneath the passageway linking the Archbishop's Palace with the Cathedral (his private access, so that he didn't have to walk on the street) and they arrived at the *Plaza del Ayuntamiento*. Looking at the buildings in that square, it was very easy to see how the three main powers were represented: political, in the *Ayuntamiento* (City Hall); religious, in the Cathedral; and judicial, in the *Palacio de la Audiencia* (Court of Justice). The main fiestas and events of the Court and the other institutions were held next to the Cathedral, while the people's celebrations took place in the *Plaza de Zocodover*.

The group stopped to admire the Cathedral's impressive main facade.

"It's an enormous building! But it's only got one tower," Ali observed.

"That's right. Only one was built. The other ended up as a dome. Can you see it? Work on the Cathedral was begun in the 18th century, in a French Gothic style, and it has later additions in the style of the local Mudéjar, Renaissance and Baroque inside. The cloister dates from the 14th century. Can you see the flying buttresses from here, in other words the arch-buttresses holding up the walls and the Gothic pinnacles? There are three entrances in the facade, each one under the pointed arches decorated with reliefs of human figures. They each have a name and the reliefs represent different scenes or symbols: the gate on your left is the Tower's; the one in the middle is the *Puerta del Perdón*, which means the Gate of Pardon, and the one on the right is called the *Puerta de los Escribanos* (of the Scriveners). You can see the rose window at the top. Large stained glass windows are very usual in Gothic cathedrals and there are many beautiful ones in this one. Let's go inside and see them!"

Once inside, the children started to wander round the Cathedral's five naves and two ambulatories. They admired their multicoloured stained glass windows, the Mudéjar wooden carvings, the Plateresque wrought iron railings, full of imperial and cardinal symbols, the Mannerist choir stalls and the two Baroque organs. Of course, the main focus of their attention was the huge figure of the giant St. Christopher carrying the child Christ on his shoulders and leaning on his stick, which was painted on the wall.

"It's a palm tree" some of the children exclaimed when they had a good look at the stick.

They also liked the clock on the wall opposite, very much Flemish in style, according to their teacher, and they were somewhat surprised by the famous altar called *El Transparente*, one of the jewels of the Baroque era, and by the tombs in the Cathedral's chapels of St. Ildephonsus and St. James, where Don Álvaro de Luna, the famous Constable of Castile, is buried.

As soon as our three friends had entered the Cathedral, they started their search. They looked everywhere to solve the old man's second enigma.

"In the chapel of St. Ildephonsus, opposite *El Transparente*," Marcos reminded them.

And the three of them went there, excited about what they might find. At first, they looked behind the railings inside the chapel, but they immediately remembered that the image was supposed to be on the ceiling in front of the chapel.

"It's a knight, with a horse and a lance!" Sara exclaimed.

"And a turban! I'm going to draw him."

"Remember to draw the shield and the horse's cloth with red and yellow stripes," Ali said to him.

Good. They had completed the second task. They were feeling very pleased with themselves.

"OK, now that we've visited the Cathedral, we're going to see the inside of a Synagogue," their teacher said, taking them towards the street called Calle de Santo Tomé. On the way, she explained to the enthusiastic children about the enormous importance the Cathedral had in every medieval city and in the Modern Age, as it was the centre of public life.

When they arrived at the Church of Santo Tomé, they turned round the corner and went along another street down towards a small square. How pleasant these small quiet streets were. On the corner there was a building open to the public.

"You can see one of the most famous paintings by El Greco here, 'The Burial of

Count Orgaz'. Who knows something about El Greco?" the teacher asked.

"He was a painter," one of the children answered.

"That's right. He was one of the most important artists in the 16th and 17th centuries because he developed a new style for religious and civil painting. It was very different to the classic style and that is why his contemporaries did not think it was very good. But today he is considered a master worldwide. His name was Domenikos Theotokopoulos. He

was born on Crete (a Greek island) and he learnt to paint in Italy with masters such as Titian and Tintoretto. He ended up working in Spain, during the reign of Philip II, with his very personal style of elongated figures."

The teacher continued to explain things connected with artistic styles to them as they went down the street called Calle de San Juan de Dios to arrive at the **Synagogue del Tránsito**.

Before they entered, she told them that there had been seven synagogues in Toledo at one time, all of them in this area of the city, called the Jewish Quarter, and that in general Jews prayed in large rooms in which the women and the men were separated and that the Torah Scrolls (the most important work in the Jewish religion containing the Five Books of Moses) were kept in a special place in one of the walls and that the faithful had to wear special clothes as well and even have ritual baths occasionally.

When the Jews, who were known as Sephardim (Sepharad was the name the Jews had given the Iberian Peninsula), were expelled from Spain in 1492, the synagogues were converted into churches. Their shape and their interior decoration were the same as the rest of the Islamic buildings, because Sephardic architecture did not have its own features and because they

were built by Muslim master builders and architects. The most outstanding feature in all of them is the decoration of carved plaster painted with plant and geometrical motifs, since both the Islamic and Jewish religions prohibited the reproduction of people as images.

"Do you know what the motifs inside mean?" the teacher asked them. "They represent nature, divine creation and paradise. Did you also know, boys and girls, that religious rites were especially important for the Jews because they were a sign of their identity as a people. They went about their daily activities as everybody else did. They spoke the same language (in addition to Hebrew),

although they lived all together in the Jewish quarters, where they had their shops, their workshops, their schools, etc. This synagogue was built during the reign of the Christian king Peter I (in the 14th century) and it was paid for by his treasurer, one of the most influential Jews in Toledo, Samuel Levi."

"Hey! This is the building where we have to look for the windows for our friend," Sara said in a low voice, just loud enough for her two friends to hear.

"Yes, we've got to go in now," Marcos replied, impatiently.

the lobes the teacher liked so much and which were all over the place in Toledo. At the back they saw the three arches in the wall leading to a niche where the Torah had been kept, surrounded with rich decoration. And a little further up in the middle of the blind arcade with two storeys of columns there were two openings letting light in: the two windows, at last!

"That's it! Now we've got the answer. Aren't they lovely! I like this synagogue!"

Sara and Ali could not stop looking all around them. And as they were also looking up, they saw the beautiful painted wooden coffered ceiling.

After a while, the children entered the Sephardic Museum, which was in the same

Once inside, they saw that the synagogue was a large room for praying in and that the area for the women was on the next floor, with several arches overlooking the room below. Opposite this large room there were others, such as the Rabbi's school, and there was a courtyard with the remains of one of the buildings where they had had their ritual baths. The large room was decorated with plaster painted with thousands of colours, with leaf and pineapple motifs and also the royal coats of arms of Peter I. There were inscriptions in very striking writing and several of those multifoil arches with all

building, and as they left they found themselves opposite another museum: the **House of El Greco**. The teacher told them the following:

"In this house they have reconstructed the rooms of a typical large house belonging to a noble family in Toledo in the 17th century using furniture and other objects from that time so that we can see the different aspects of their lives: what their bedrooms were like, their offices, how they cooked and served their food, etc."

The children continued walking to the place where the bus was going to pick them up, the Bridge of San Martin. What a coincidence! They went along the street called Calle de los Reyes Católicos and they went in front of a lovely Modernist building dating from the 19th century, the School of Arts and Trades, and they also went by the even more wonderful Monastery of San Juan de los Reyes.

The group stopped to eat their sandwiches at last in the small square leading to the bridge. It had been a long trek! Sara, Ali and Marcos couldn't stop thinking about the fact that they had to meet the mysterious old man right here.

Marcos was finishing off his drawing of the two windows in the Synagogue when Ali saw the silhouette of their new friend slowly making his way towards them in the distance. The three friends ran to meet him and noticed that he looked tired, but happy.

"I'm very pleased to see you here, children, at the appointed time! Did you manage to find what I asked you to do?"

"Yes, of course!" the three of them almost shouted in unison. "Here's the capital in the Mosque, the knight in the Cathedral and the two windows in the Synagogue."

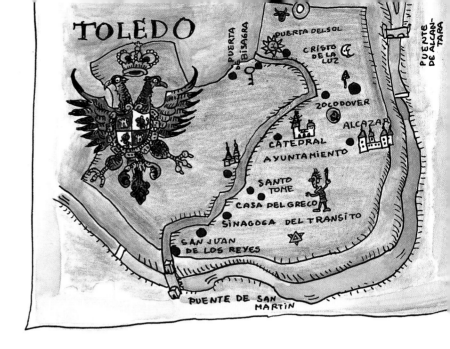

"That's fantastic, children. Well done! I don't know how to thank you. You've been a great help to me, really you have. I'm going to be able to finish my 'memoirs' correctly now because, although I took part in constructing and decorating all those buildings, that was all a very long time ago now and I find it difficult to remember everything."

The children looked at each other in surprise and they exclaimed: "Come on! That can't be true! How could you have lived in such different ages?"

And the old man replied enigmatically: "My memory can embrace all the ages, as can the memory of the city of the three cultures."

The children winked at each other and whispered confidently: "It must be because he's so old."

"Well, did you like Toledo?" the stallkeeper asked them, changing the subject.

"Yes, a lot! It's a city with a great deal of history," Sara said.

"And a heritage that has to be looked after and explained, doesn't it? Not only because it's so beautiful and interesting, but above all because it demonstrates that, at the same time and in the same city, human beings with different beliefs, customs and cultures can find those things that make them the same and manage to make these the ones they use to live together and share expectations, hopes, everyday problems and their solutions. This city's history can teach us so many things, can't it?"

"Of course! We will never forget it."

The three children went back home to their classes, their teachers and their families having had an exciting, magical and, above all, educational day. Tiredness overtook them on the journey back, yet they all dreamt (with their eyes open or closed) of busy streets, full of people with different names and beliefs, but wearing the same clothes, carrying the same objects in their hands, doing the same things and toing and froing from their homes to their shops, the fields or their workshops, to school, to the synagogue, the mosque or the church, to annual fiestas, to public baths, to...